Contents

*C = copper; B = bronze; S = silver; T = teacher; ( ) = the line must be played but cannot be assessed for a Medal.

In a Minor Mode

Bob Power

AB 3039

Pourquoi?

Cornelius Bruinsma

AB 3039

Shearplace Hill

Stephen Kenyon

Shearplace Hill is a small Bronze Age site in Dorset.

Little Star

Bob Power

AB 3039

A Village Wedding

Debbie Cracknell

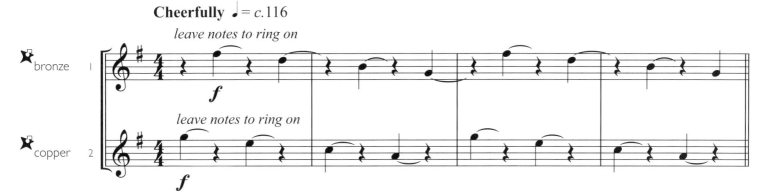

Rain Dance

Richard Wright

AB 3039

Pastime

Vincent Lindsey-Clark

AB 3039

Promenade

Jonathan Leathwood

AB 3039

Mexican Jumping-Bean

Derek Hasted

Beat Route

Debbie Cracknell

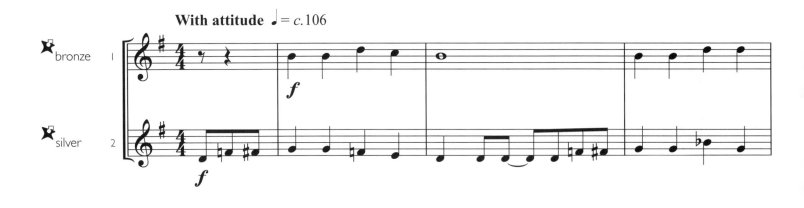

AB 3039

Indian Warrior Chief

Cornelius Bruinsma

Canzona

Richard Wright

AB 3039

Caterpillar Clog Dance

Derek Hasted

$\times$ = Tap the body of the guitar to make a percussive sound of your choice.
The spoken words are optional for the Medal.

Woodruff

Jane Bentley

AB 3039

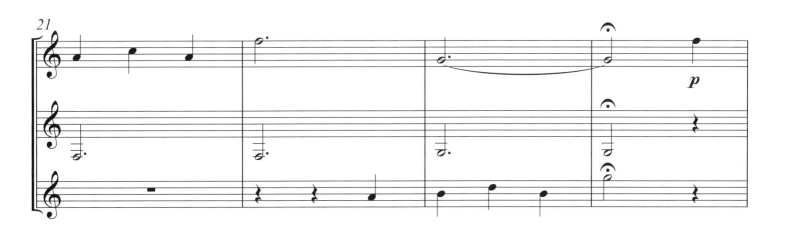

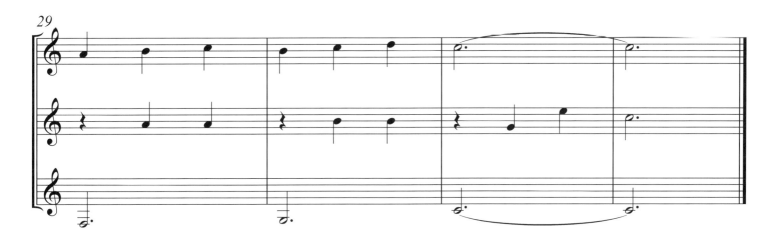

Chant would be a fine thing

Vincent Lindsey-Clark

AB 3039

Costa Brava

Fran Gray

☒ ☒ ☒ = Tap the body of the guitar to make a percussive sound of your choice.

☒ = Stamp your right foot.

for Ann Comper

The Bells of St Anne's

Jonathan Leathwood

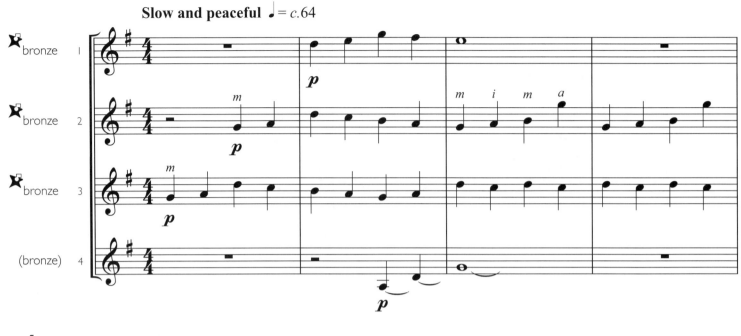

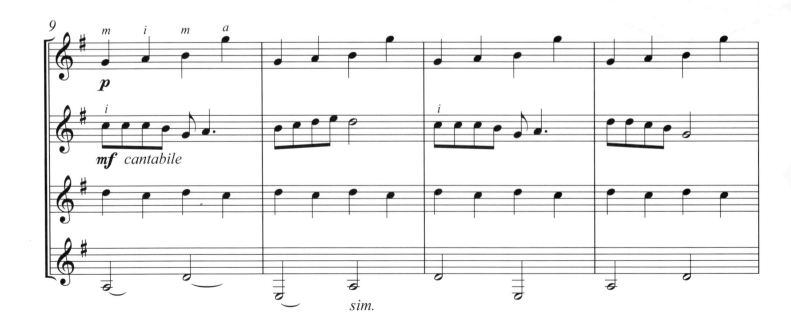

AB 3039

Claret and Blues

Stephen Goss

♩ = Slap bass strings against frets with side of thumb.

AB 3039